Free

Story by Kathleen Gibson
Illustrations by Vickie Glenn

One day Jimmy caught a butterfly
and put it in a jar.

"Let it go," said his mother.
"A butterfly needs flowers."
"No," said Jimmy, "I want to keep it."

"It should be free," said his father.
"A butterfly needs to fly."
"I want to keep it," said Jimmy.

Jimmy took his butterfly to school.
His teacher said, "A butterfly needs
flowers and water and air."
Jimmy said, "I'll keep it in my jar."

Then Jimmy looked at the butterfly.
He thought and thought.
"You need to be free."

"There it goes!"
"It's free to fly!"